A Combined - Harves

C000241737

BEAUTIFUL WORLD

Words and Music by
Paul Field

With energy ♩ = 130

1. From the cro-co-diles and
(2.) snow up-on the moun-

kan - ga-roos_ to the birds and bum-ble-bees,_ from the
- tain - tops_ to the fruit up-on_ the trees,_ from the

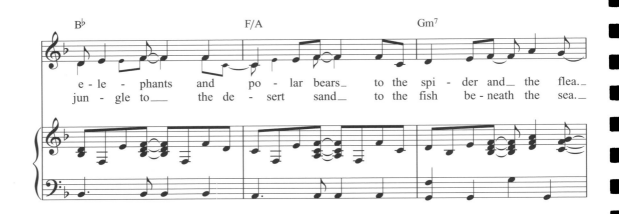

e - le - phants and po - lar bears_ to the spi - der and_ the flea.
jun - gle to_ the de - sert sand_ to the fish be - neath the sea.

It's a - maz - - ing,___ the
It's a - (%)maz - - ing,___ the

won - der of___ cre - a - tion and we all just
won - der of___ cre - a - tion and we've all a

want to___ say... }
part to___ play. }

Thank you for the morn - ing light,_ thank you for the moon-

4

2. From the world you made.

D. 𝄋 *al Coda*

It's a -

CODA

world, a beau - ti - ful world, it's a

beau - ti - ful world you made.

BIG RED COMBINE HARVESTER

Words and Music by
Niki Davies

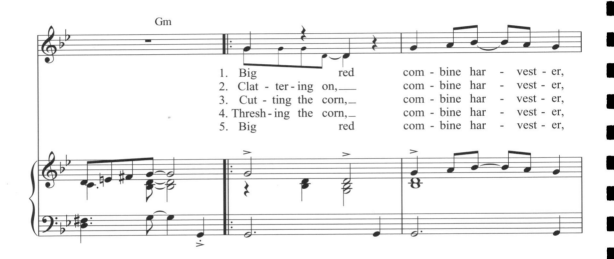

1. Big   red   com - bine har - vest - er,
2. Clat - ter - ing on,__ com - bine har - vest - er,
3. Cut - ting the corn,__ com - bine har - vest - er,
4. Thresh - ing the corn,__ com - bine har - vest - er,
5. Big   red   com - bine har - vest - er,

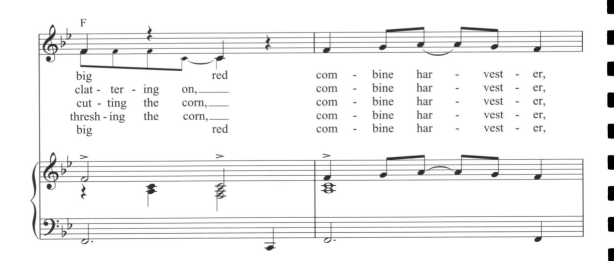

big   red   com - bine har - vest - er,
clat - ter - ing on,__ com - bine har - vest - er,
cut - ting the corn,__ com - bine har - vest - er,
thresh - ing the corn,__ com - bine har - vest - er,
big   red   com - bine har - vest - er,

big ____ red ____ com - bine har - vest - er,
clat - ter - ing on, ____ com - bine har - vest - er,
cut - ting the corn, ____ com - bine har - vest - er,
thresh - ing the corn, ____ com - bine har - vest - er,
big ____ red ____ com - bine har - vest - er,

chug, chug, chug, chug, chug - ging a - way. ____
chug, chug, chug, chug, chug - ging a - way. ____
chug, chug, chug, chug, chug - ging a - way. ____
chug, chug, chug, chug, chug - ging a - way. ____
chug, chug, chug, chug, chug - ging a - way. ____

Chug, chug, chug, chug, chug - ging a - way. ____

CEREALS, BREAD, VEG AND FRUIT

Words and Music by
Anne Blackwell and Niki Davies

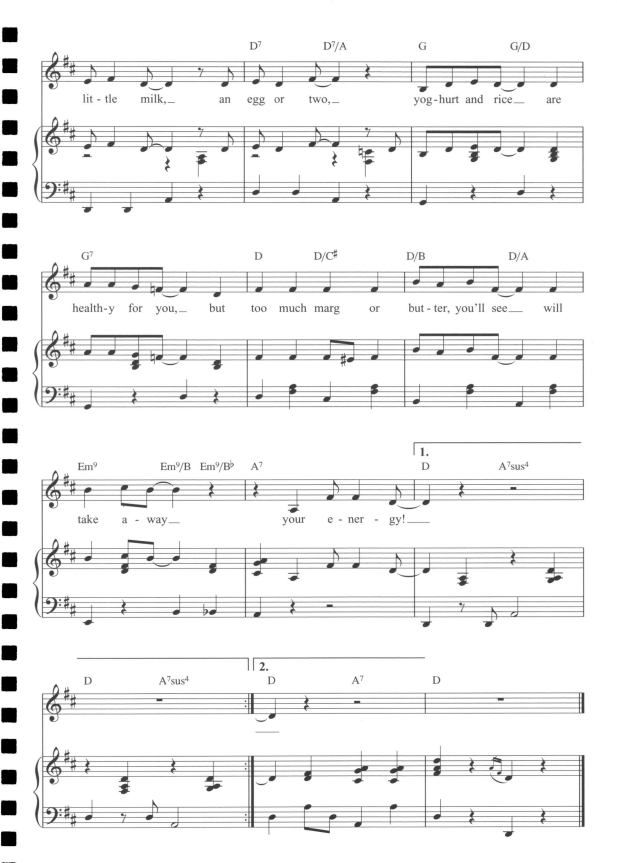

CONKERS!

Words and Music by
Mark and Helen Johnson

Con-kers! I'm col-lect-ing con-kers, I'm try-ing hard to find the big-gest and the best. Con-kers! Lots of love-ly

EVERYWHERE AROUND ME

Words and Music by
Mark and Helen Johnson

1. Tell me who made all____ of cre - a - tion,
2. Tell me who made mu - sic and laugh - ter,
3. Don't stop look - ing, don't____ stop be - liev - ing,

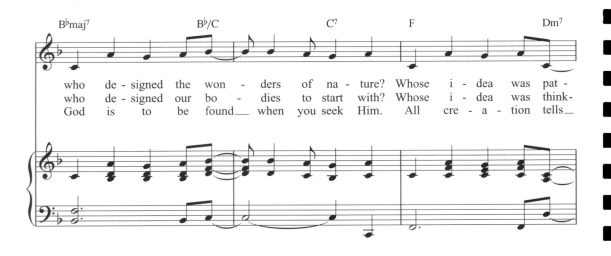

who de-signed the won-ders of na-ture? Whose i-dea was pat-
who de-signed our bo-dies to start with? Whose i-dea was think-
God is to be found___ when you seek Him. All cre-a-tion tells___

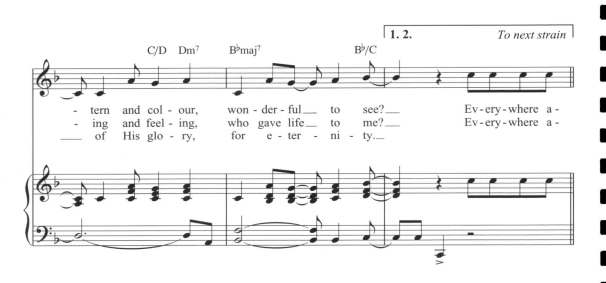

1. 2. *To next strain*

-tern and col-our, won-der-ful___ to see?___ Ev-ery-where a-
-ing and feel-ing, who gave life___ to me?___ Ev-ery-where a-
___ of His glo-ry, for e-ter-ni-ty.___

3.

Ev-ery-where a-round me

I can see the hand__ of God,__ the e - vi - dence sur-

-rounds me in the great - ness of__ His world.__

1. 3. 5.

Ev - ery - where a -

2. 4.

D. 𝄊

6.

Ev - ery - where a - round me!

EVERYBODY PRAISE HIM

Words and Music by
Mark and Helen Johnson

FIVE A DAY

Words and Music by
Niki Davies

One, two, three, four, five a day,__ one, two, three, four, five a day,__ it's got to be__ the health-y way, it's one, two, three, four, five, five a day.__

1. Ap - ples   and ba - na - nas too,__
2. Ki - wi   fruit and peach - es too,__
3. Cab - ba - ges__ and   car - rots too,__
4. Let - tuce   and to - ma - toes too,__

you can take your pick. Straw-ber-ries and man-goes,
you can take your pick. Or-ang-es and jui-cy pears,
you can take your pick. Au-ber-gines and French beans,
you can take your pick. Ra-di-shes and shi-ny peas,

1. 2. 3.

these should do the trick.
these should do the trick.
these should do the trick.

4.

these should do the trick.

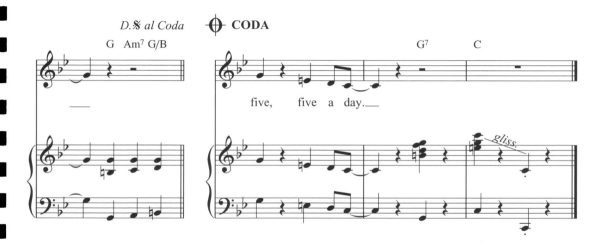

D.%. al Coda   **CODA**

five, five a day.

FOOD COLOURS

Words and Music by
Mark and Helen Johnson

Starting steadily, getting faster each verse ♩ = 88-104

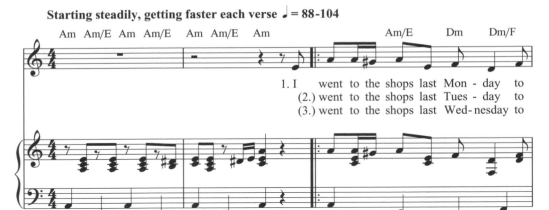

1. I went to the shops last Mon - day to
(2.) went to the shops last Tues - day to
(3.) went to the shops last Wed - nesday to

buy my Mum some food. She said would I make it health - y,
buy my Gran some food. She said would I make it health - y, } 'cause
buy my Dad some food. He said would I make it health - y,

col - our - ings aren't so good. I went past the crisps and co - la to

find the veg and fruit, the shelves were so full of col-ours, I did-n't know what to do! I

bought { her / him } a bag of or - ang - es, some greens and le - mons too. I

tried ve-ry hard but could-n't find a - ny blacks or

1. 2. accel.

blues!

2. I blues!
3. I

3.

21

Good Things

Words and Music by
Mark and Helen Johnson

1. Bak - ing bread, coun - try air,
3. Cloud - less skies, moun - tain views,
5. Sing - ing birds, warm "Hel - los",

fresh - ly laun - dered clothes to wear, ti - dy lawns, ro -
when some - bo - dy smiles at you, a page of ticks, plates
mu - sic on the ra - di - o, loud gui - tars, sax -

- ses fair, smell so good_ to me.
__ of food look so good_ to me.
- o - phones sound so good_ to me.

2. Ten - der hands, silk — y sheets, gen - tle sand_ be - neath_
4. Jui - cy fruit — good_ to eat, bars of choc - olate, bags_

__ my _ feet, sooth - ing baths, sum - mer breeze,
__ of_sweets, fizz - y drinks in_ the heat

feel so good___ to me.
taste so good___ to me.

There are so ma-ny good___

___ things for___ us to ap - pre - ci - ate.

Ev - ery - bo - dy join in___ the cho - rus, we can ce - le - brate!___

There are so ma-ny good___ things for___ us to ap-pre-ci-ate. Ev-ery-bo-dy join in___ the cho-rus, we can ce-le-brate!___

There are so ma-ny good___things for___ us,

to ap-pre - ci - ate.

Thank the Lord for his lov-

- ing kind - ness each and ev - ery day!___

HARVEST SAMBA

Words and Music by
Mark and Helen Johnson

2. Ap - ri - cots and plums, ri - pened in__ the sun,
4. Cof - fee, co - coa, tea, grow - ing na - t'ral - ly,

or - ang - es__ and yel - low ba - na - nas, good for ev - ery - one!
her - bal plants and all__ kinds of spi - ces, ve - ry nice__ in - deed!

It's a - no - ther Har - vest Fes - ti - val when we bring our fruit and

vege - ta - bles, 'cause we want to share the best of all__ the good__

G G/B Em Em/G Em/B Am Am/C B7
vege - ta - bles, 'cause we want to share the best of all__ the good__
food we eat, with a sam - ba ce - le - bra - tion to__ say 'Thank__
B7/D# B7/F# 1. Em Em/G Em/B Em 2. Em B Em7
__ things that we've been giv - en.__ Fa - ther,__
__ you' to God the
B Em B Em7 B
God the
Em B Em7 B Em B Em
Fa - ther.__

HARVEST SONG

Words and Music by
Mark and Helen Johnson

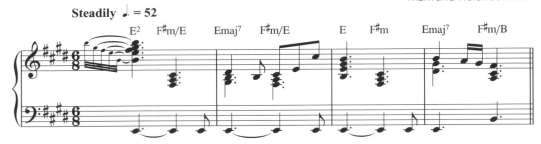

1. There is a far-mer who stands in his fields and he sees all the work to be
2. There was a time when the fields were pre-pared and the good soil was care-ful-ly
3. There was some time for the far-mer to wait as the seeds slow-ly grew out of
4. Now is the time when the crops are full grown and the far-mer must ga-ther them

done.____ He has been watch-ing for ma-ny a month, he's been
ploughed.__ Then came the day_ for the far-mer to sow_ and the
sight.____ Then came the day_ when the first shoots ap-peared and the
in.____ He'll need some help_ 'cause there's lots to be done_ and it's

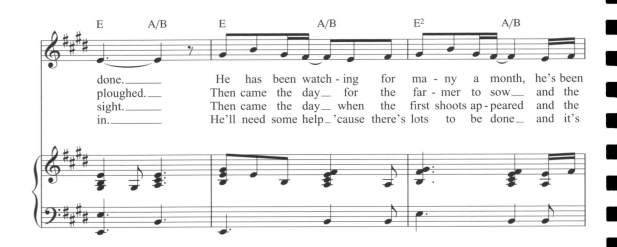

waiting for this day to come.
seeds were all scat-tered a-round.
far-mer was filled with de-light.
hard to know where to be-gin.

There's a song to sing as the har-

-vest comes in, to the One who gives sun-shine and rain._____ Let us

Last time to Coda ⊕

all join in with a thank - of-fer-ing__ for the har-vest that's gath-ered a-

1. 2. 3.
-gain.__

4. *D.%̸ al Coda*
-gain. There's a

⊕ **CODA**

rit.
-gain.__

HARVEST HYMN
(GIVE THANKS)

Words and Music by
Mark and Helen Johnson

Smoothly ♩ = 112

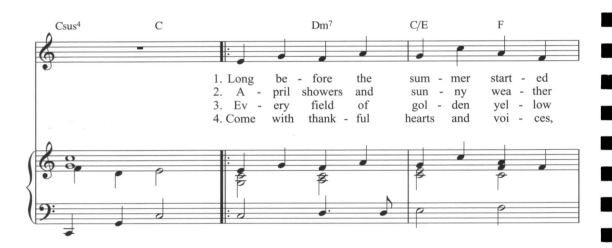

1. Long be - fore the sum - mer start - ed
2. A - pril showers and sun - ny wea - ther
3. Ev - ery field of gol - den yel - low
4. Come with thank - ful hearts and voi - ces,

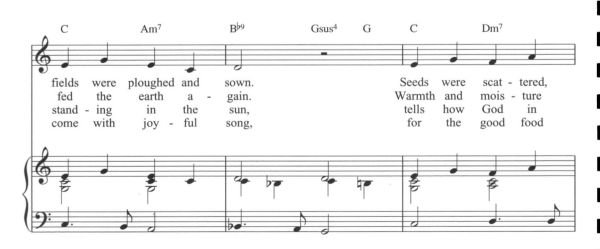

fields were ploughed and sown.   Seeds were scat - tered,
fed the earth a - gain.   Warmth and mois - ture
stand - ing in the sun,   tells how God in
come with joy - ful song,   for the good food

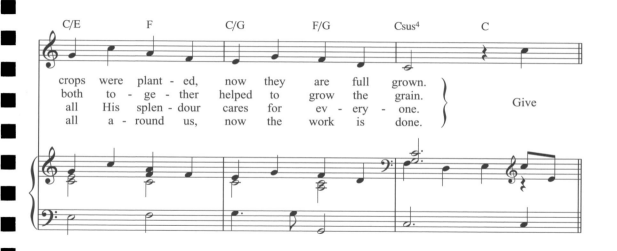

crops were plant - ed, now they are full grown.
both to - ge - ther helped to grow the grain.
all His splen - dour cares for ev - ery - one.
all a - round us, now the work is done.

Give

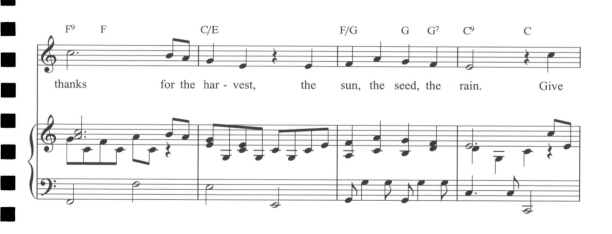

thanks for the har - vest, the sun, the seed, the rain. Give

1. 2. 3.

thanks_____ to God the Fa - ther for har - vest time a - gain.

4.

Csus⁴   C   B♭/C   C   F⁹   F   C⁹/E   C/E

-gain.   Give   thanks   for   the   har - vest,   the

F/G   G   G⁷   C⁹   Am/C   C⁷   F   F♯dim⁷

sun,   the   seed,   the   rain.   Give   thanks_____   to   God   the

C/G   Am   Dm⁷   G⁷   C   Dm⁷

Fa - ther   for   har - vest   time   a - gain.

rall.

C/E   F   C/G   Dm/G   Csus⁴   C

38

HARVEST TIME HAS COME

Words and Music by
Sha Armstrong

The far-mer's in his fields from dawn till dusk, work-ing ev-ery hour as he

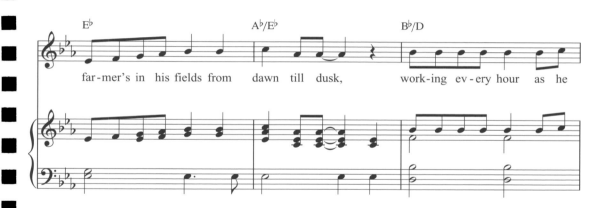

knows he must, gath-'ring all the crops till the work is done, for

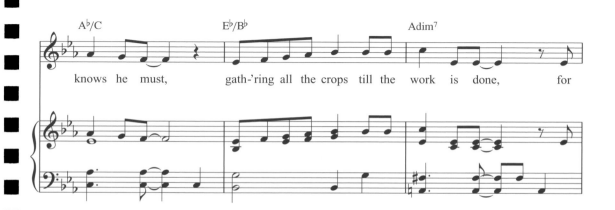

food   we   love   to   eat.   Dig-ging   up   the   car - rots,
food   we   love   to   eat.   Dig-ging   up   the   pars - nips,
food   we   love   to   eat.   Dig-ging   up   po - ta - toes,

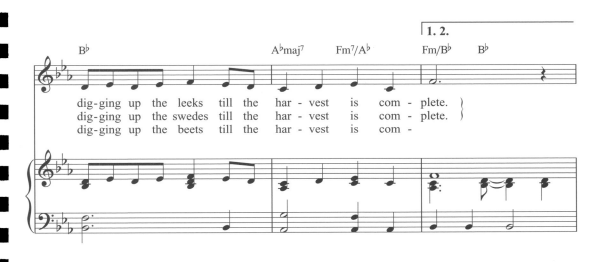

dig-ging   up   the   leeks   till   the   har - vest   is   com - plete.)
dig-ging   up   the   swedes   till   the   har - vest   is   com - plete.)
dig-ging   up   the   beets   till   the   har - vest   is   com -

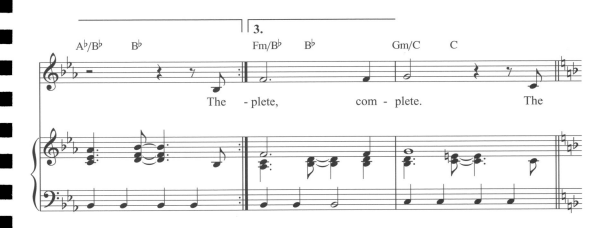

The   - plete,   com - plete.   The

IN MY TROLLEY

Words and Music by
Jeff Hammer

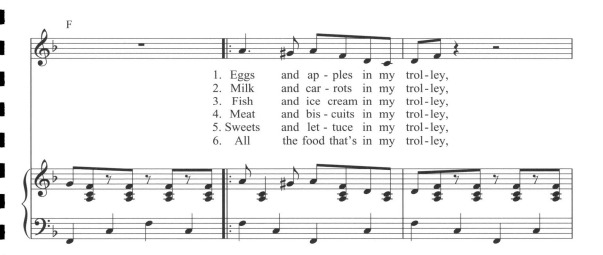

1. Eggs and ap - ples in my trol - ley,
2. Milk and car - rots in my trol - ley,
3. Fish and ice cream in my trol - ley,
4. Meat and bis - cuits in my trol - ley,
5. Sweets and let - tuce in my trol - ley,
6. All the food that's in my trol - ley,

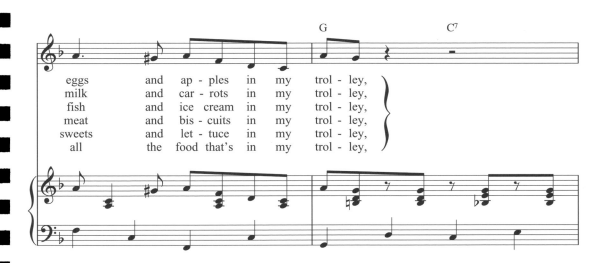

eggs and ap - ples in my trol - ley,
milk and car - rots in my trol - ley,
fish and ice cream in my trol - ley,
meat and bis - cuits in my trol - ley,
sweets and let - tuce in my trol - ley,
all the food that's in my trol - ley,

fish and ice cream, milk and car-rots, eggs and ap-ples in my

trol-ley. sweets and let-tuce, meat and bis-cuits,

fish and ice cream, milk and car-rots, eggs and ap-ples in my

trol-ley. all the food that's in my trol-ley.

LUNCHTIME QUEUE

Words and Music by
Mark and Helen Johnson

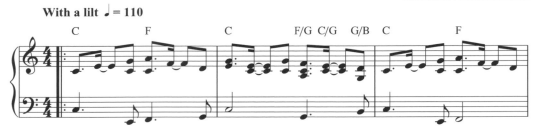

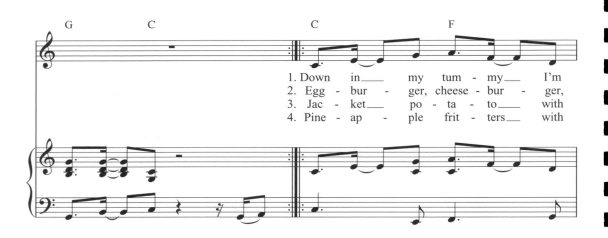

1. Down in___ my tum - my___ I'm
2. Egg - bur - ger, cheese - bur - ger,
3. Jac - ket___ po - ta - to___ with
4. Pine - ap - ple frit - ters___ with

feel - ing___ so hun - gry, my mind is___ on no - thing___ but
bar - be - cued bean - bur - ger, gua - ran - teed lean, served with
sal - ad___ that tastes so de - li - cious___ with may - o___ and
ba - na - na split - ters___ and rasp - ber - ry rip - ple___ served

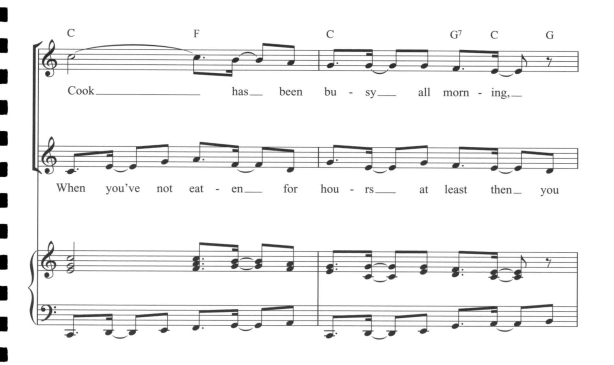

Cook_____ has_ been bu - sy_ all morn - ing,_

When you've not eat - en_ for hou - rs_ at least then_ you

her_____ food will have to_ do! have to_ do!

can't help_ but dream in_ the lunch-time_ queue!

MR SCARECROW

Words and Music by
Niki Davies

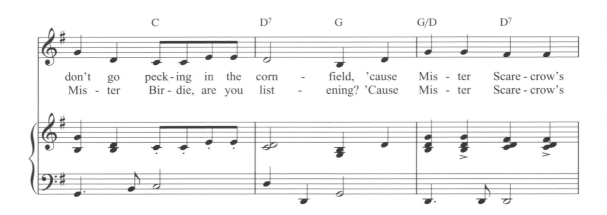

there! } Mis – ter Scare - crow, Mis – ter Scare - crow,

Mis – ter Scare - crow is wait – ing for

1. 3. 5.   **2. 4. 6.**

you.   Mis – ter you!

PICTURE OF AUTUMN

Words and Music by
Mary Green and Julie Stanley

We can sing a pic-ture of

au - tumn, we can paint a me - lo - dy,

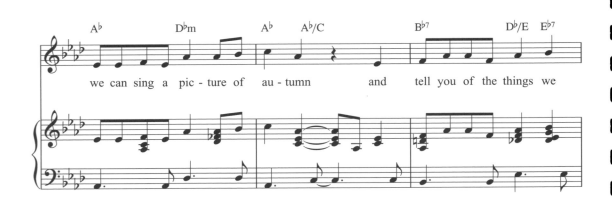

we can sing a pic-ture of au-tumn and tell you of the things we

CCLI Song No. 5182750

PRAISE TO THE ONE

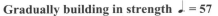

Words and Music by
Mark and Helen Johnson

Gradually building in strength ♩. = 57

Praise to the One who made our_ bo - dies, praise to the One who

SING A SONG FOR HARVEST

Words and Music by
Nikki Lewis

Steadily ♩ = 126

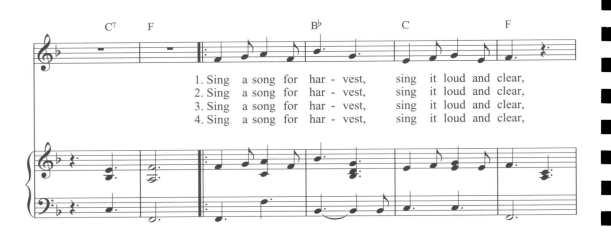

1. Sing a song for har - vest, sing it loud and clear,
2. Sing a song for har - vest, sing it loud and clear,
3. Sing a song for har - vest, sing it loud and clear,
4. Sing a song for har - vest, sing it loud and clear,

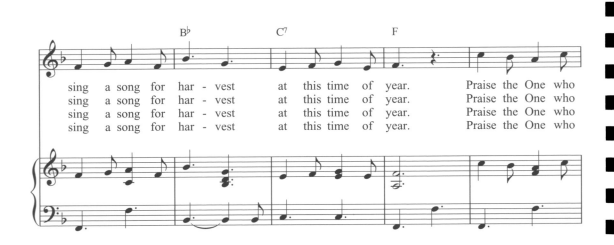

sing a song for har - vest at this time of year. Praise the One who
sing a song for har - vest at this time of year. Praise the One who
sing a song for har - vest at this time of year. Praise the One who
sing a song for har - vest at this time of year. Praise the One who

SUPER SUN

Words and Music by
Niki Davies

ber-ries nice__ and mel-low, su - per sun,__
fruit tastes e - ven bet-ter, su - per sun,__
gol-den hay__ stay dri-er, su - per sun,__

1. 2.
su - per sun.__
su - per sun.__

3.
su - per sun.__

Su - per sun!__

THANK YOU FOR ALMOST EVERYTHING!

Words and Music by
Mary Green and Julie Stanley

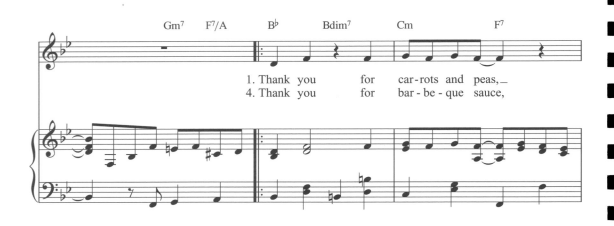

1. Thank you for car-rots and peas,—
4. Thank you for bar-be-que sauce,

thank you for ho-ney from bees,— thank you for
thank you for ket-chup of course, thank you for

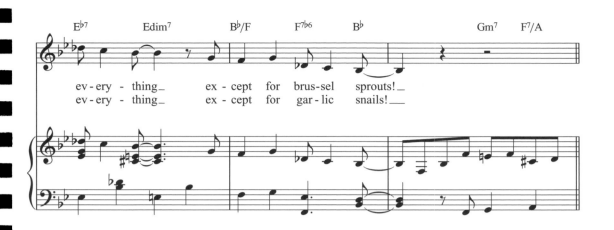

ev - ery - thing___ ex - cept for brus-sel sprouts!___
ev - ery - thing___ ex - cept for gar - lic snails!___

2. Thank you for cur - ry and rice,___ thank you for
5. Thank you for chic-ken to roast,___ thank you for

straw - ber - ry ice,___ thank you for ev - ery - thing___ ex -
baked beans on toast,___ thank you for ev - ery - thing___ ex -

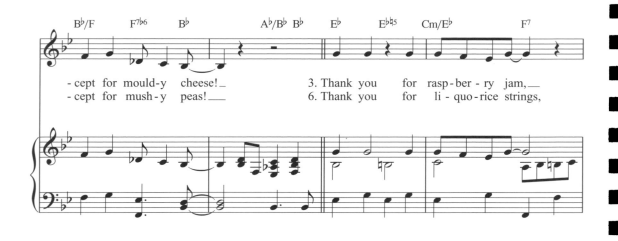

-cept for mould-y cheese! _   3. Thank you   for rasp-ber-ry jam, __
-cept for mush-y peas! __   6. Thank you   for li-quo-rice strings,

thank you   for   ba-con and ham, _   thank you   for
thank you   for   choc-ola-ty things,   thank you   for

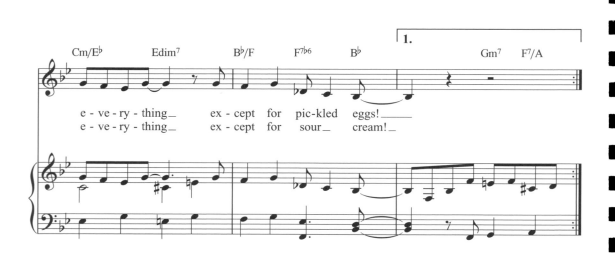

e - ve-ry - thing_   ex-cept for pic-kled eggs! ____
e - ve-ry - thing_   ex-cept for sour_ cream! _

2.

7. Thank you for sau-sage and chips,

thank you for grapes with no pips, ___

thank you for ev-er-y-thing, ___ *Spoken: Well, almost everything,*

al-most ev-er-y-thing! ___

THANK YOU FOR THE SUNSHINE

Words and Music by
Mark and Helen Johnson

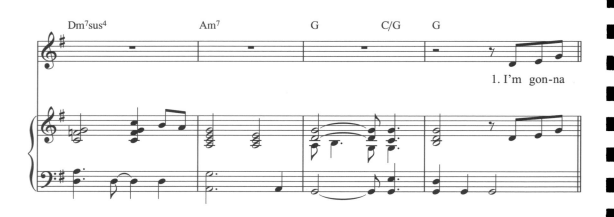

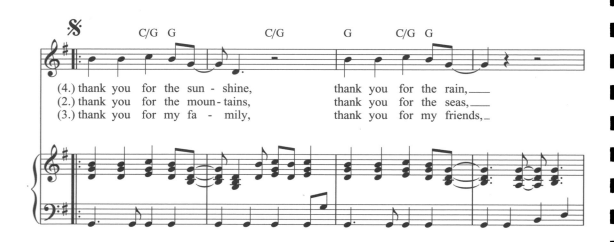

(4.) thank you for the sun - shine, thank you for the rain,___
(2.) thank you for the moun - tains, thank you for the seas,___
(3.) thank you for my fa - mily, thank you for my friends,_

thank you in the bright times and the dark times.
thank you for the big things and the small things.
thank you for the times we share to - ge - ther.

I'm gon-na thank you ev - ery morn - ing,
I'm gon-na thank you for cre - a - tion, the
I'm gon-na thank you for be - gin - nings and

thank you ev - ery day, thank you in the good
ve - ry air we breathe, thank you for the beau -
when things have to end, thank you for the love

things we've been giv - en,

so ma - ny rea - sons to___ be glad.___

1. 2.

3.

D.%̸ al Coda

2. I'm gon-na
3. I'm gon-na

4. I'm gon-na

CODA

rit.

Thank you in the good___times and the hard___times.

THANK YOU GOD FOR THE HARVEST

Words and Music by
Niki Davies

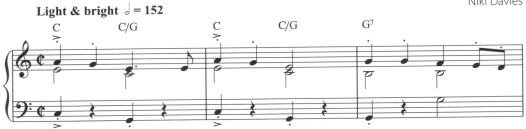

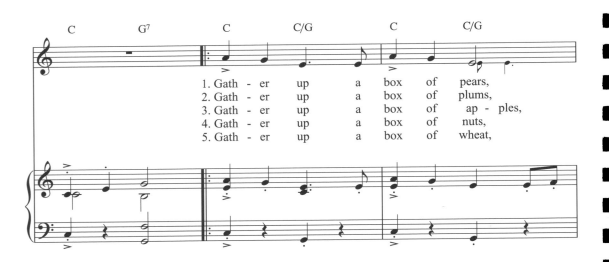

1. Gath - er up a box of pears,
2. Gath - er up a box of plums,
3. Gath - er up a box of ap - ples,
4. Gath - er up a box of nuts,
5. Gath - er up a box of wheat,

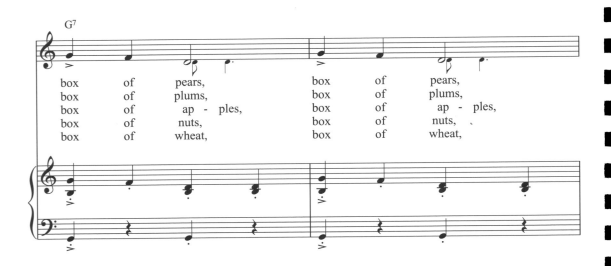

box of pears, box of pears,
box of plums, box of plums,
box of ap - ples, box of ap - ples,
box of nuts, box of nuts,
box of wheat, box of wheat,

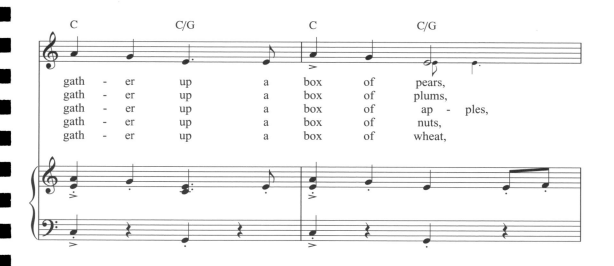

gath - er up a box of pears,
gath - er up a box of plums,
gath - er up a box of ap - ples,
gath - er up a box of nuts,
gath - er up a box of wheat,

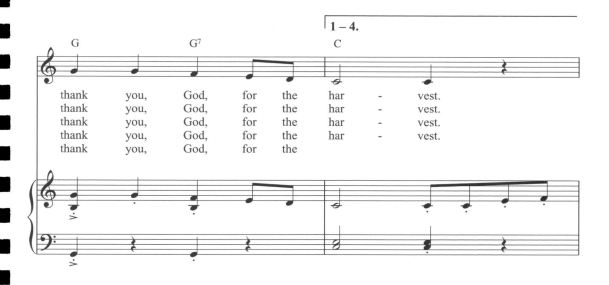

1 – 4.

thank you, God, for the har - vest.
thank you, God, for the har - vest.
thank you, God, for the har - vest.
thank you, God, for the har - vest.
thank you, God, for the

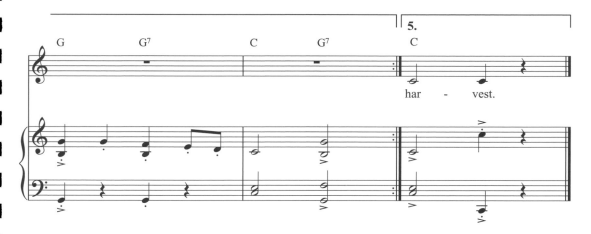

5.

har - vest.

THE HARVEST OF LOVE

Words and Music by
Mary Green and Julie Stanley

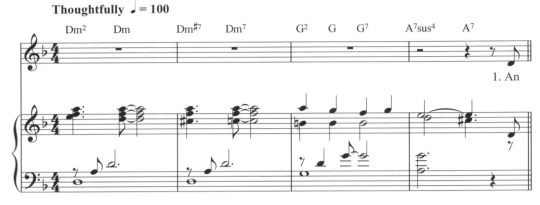

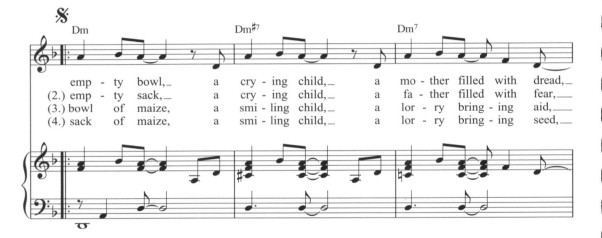

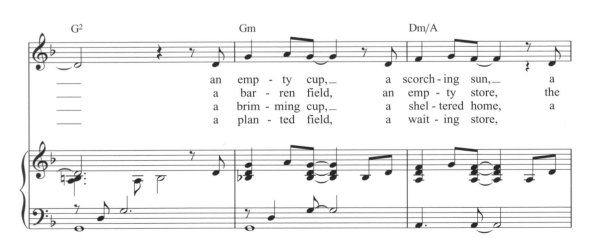

1. 3.

dried up riv - er bed.____

dif - ference has been made.____

2. An

4. A

2. 4.

crops have failed this

hope for those in

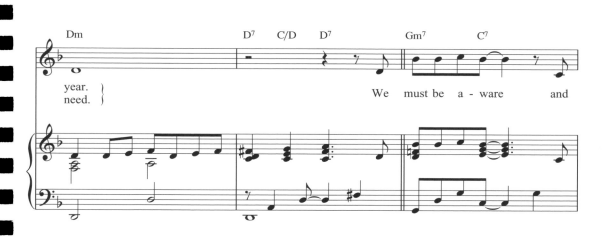

year.
need.

We must be a - ware and

show that we care,____ so let's work to-ge-ther in this world we share. Let's

THE HEALTHY HABANERA

Words and Music by
Mary Green and Julie Stanley

1. You must eat your fruit and veg you know,—
2. Have a car-rot or a tan - ge - rine,—

make you strong and help your bo - dy grow,—
have a man-go or an au - ber-gine,—

eyes will spar-kle and your skin will glow—
chew on veg-gies that are shades of green—

when you eat your five a day.
and you'll get your five a day.

Just be a-ware if you long for shi-ny hair,

eat lots and lots and you won't come out in spots!

THE SUN CAME SHINING DOWN

Words and Music by
Niki Davies

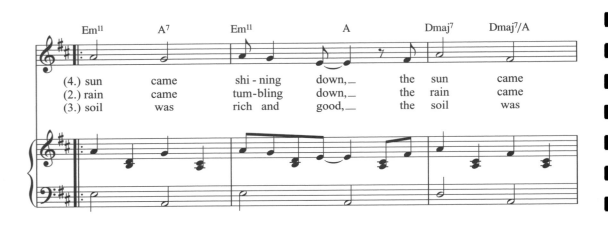

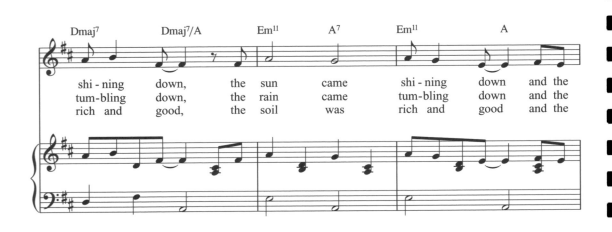

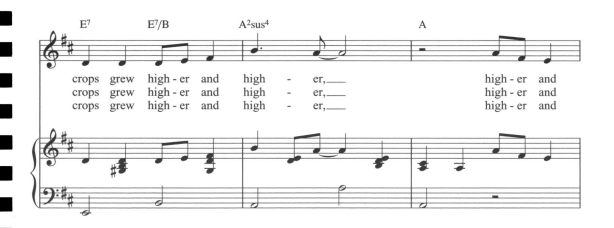

crops grew high - er and high - er,___ high - er and
crops grew high - er and high - er,___ high - er and
crops grew high - er and high - er,___ high - er and

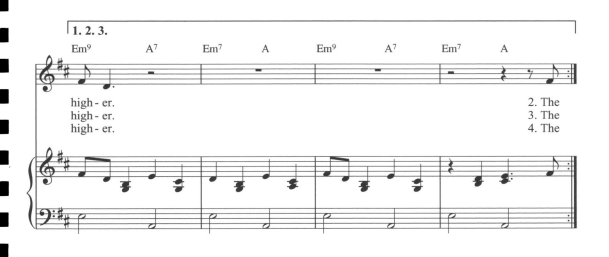

1. 2. 3.

high - er.   2. The
high - er.   3. The
high - er.   4. The

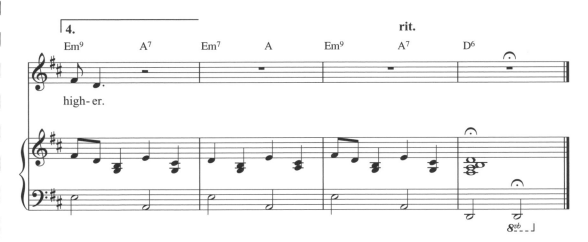

4.   rit.

high- er.

THE VEGETABLE SONG

Words and Music by
Paul Field

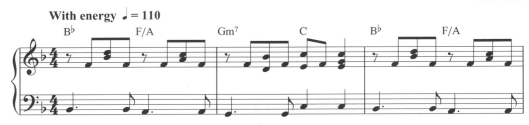

1. I like vege-ta-bles, they
2. I like vege-ta-bles, they're
3. I like vege-ta-bles, there's

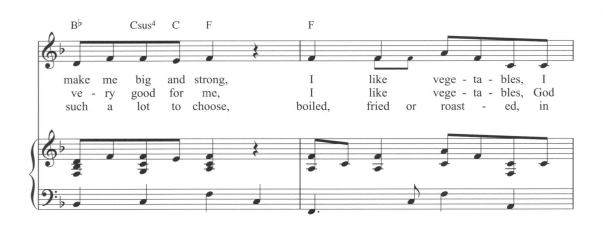

make me big and strong, I like vege-ta-bles, I
ve-ry good for me, I like vege-ta-bles, God
such a lot to choose, boiled, fried or roast-ed, in

eat them all day long,   spi - nach and car - rots,
made them all you see,   mush - rooms and sweet - corn, po-
cas - se - roles and stews,   o - nions and au - ber - gines,

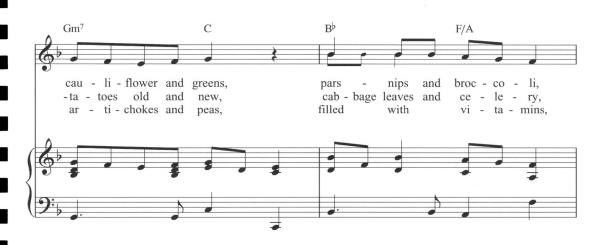

cau - li - flower and greens,   pars - nips and broc - co - li,
-ta - toes old and new,   cab - bage leaves and ce - le - ry,
ar - ti - chokes and peas,   filled with vi - ta - mins,

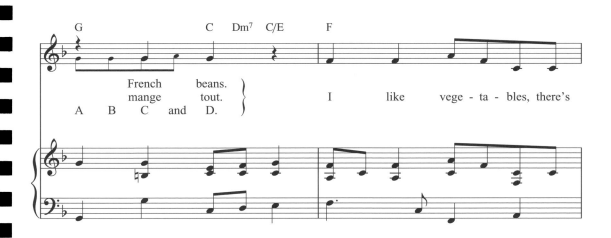

French beans.
mange tout.
A   B   C   and   D.

I like vege - ta - bles, there's

WE THANK YOU

Words and Music by
Sha Armstrong

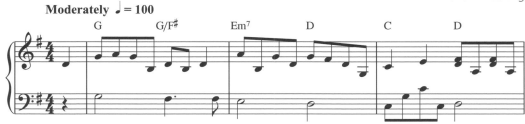

We thank you God for all___ you have giv-en us,

fa - milies, food and friends. We thank you God for

all you have giv-en us, for all you've made, we

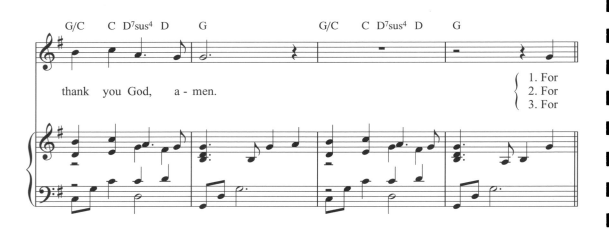

thank you God, a - men.

1. For
2. For
3. For

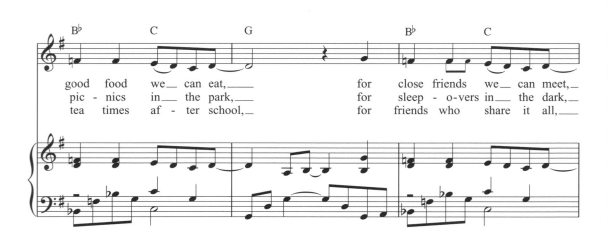

good food we_ can eat,___ for close friends we_ can meet,__
pic - nics in__ the park,__ for sleep - o-vers in__ the dark,__
tea times af - ter school,_ for friends who share it all,__

for fa - milies all___ a - round___ who
for fa - milies ev - ery - where, we
for fa - milies, yours and mine,___ who

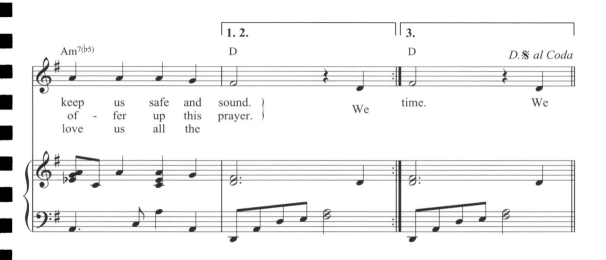

1. 2. **3.**

D   D   *D.% al Coda*

keep us safe and sound. } We time. We
of - fer up this prayer.
love us all the

CODA

rit.

thank you God, a - men.

83

WEIRD AND WONDERFUL

Words and Music by
Paul Field

1. Where is the pie in a pine-ap-ple?
2. Have you tas-ted hot goat cur-ry?

Who made ba-na-nas bent? Just how fast can a
Did you try a horse meat stew? Have you had a duck's foot

run-ner bean run?   Why   does a cau-li-flow-er   have no scent?
braised   in   brine   or   kan-ga-roo   steak   on the   bar - be-que?_   It's a

weird   and   won-der-ful world,_   full of tastes   so   bit-ter and

sweet,   it's a   weird   and   won-der-ful world_   of   food   with

so   much   choice   of good things to eat._   good things to eat._

To Coda ⊕   **1.**   **2.**

85

86

WHAT YOU SOW

Words and Music by
Ann Beresford

Confidently ♩ = 138

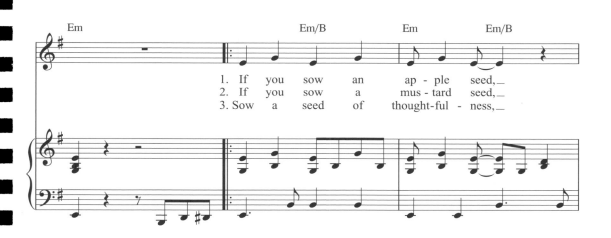

1. If you sow an ap - ple seed,__
2. If you sow a mus - tard seed,__
3. Sow a seed of thought-ful - ness,__

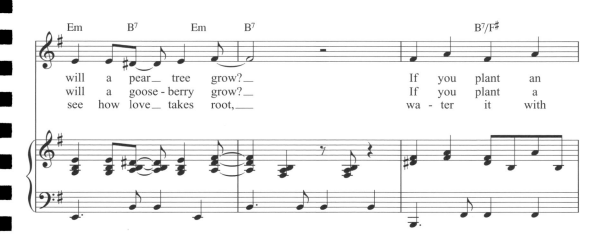

will a pear__ tree grow?__ If you plant an
will a goose - berry grow?__ If you plant a
see how love__ takes root,___ wa - ter it with

BEAUTIFUL WORLD

Words and Music by Paul Field

1   From the crocodiles and kangaroos
To the birds and bumblebees,
From the elephants and polar bears
To the spider and the flea.
It's amazing, the wonder of creation
And we all just want to say…

CHORUS   *Thank you for the morning light,*
Thank you for the moonlit night,
Thank you for the sunshine and the rain.
Thank you for the hope you bring,
Thank you God for everything,
It's a beautiful world you made.

2   From the snow upon the mountaintops
To the fruit upon the trees,
From the jungle to the desert sand
To the fish beneath the sea.
It's amazing, the wonder of creation
And we've all a part to play.

CHORUS

It's amazing, the wonder of creation
And we've all a part to play.

LAST CHORUS
Thank you for the morning light,
Thank you for the moonlit night,
Thank you for the sunshine and the rain.
Thank you for the hope you bring,
Thank you God for everything,
It's a beautiful world,
A beautiful world,
It's a beautiful world you made.

Big Red Combine Harvester

Words and Music by Niki Davies

1   Big red combine harvester,
Big red combine harvester,
Big red combine harvester,
Chug, chug, chug, chug, chugging away.

2   Clattering on, combine harvester,
Clattering on, combine harvester,
Clattering on, combine harvester,
Chug, chug, chug, chug, chugging away.

3   Cutting the corn, combine harvester,
Cutting the corn, combine harvester,
Cutting the corn, combine harvester,
Chug, chug, chug, chug, chugging away.

4   Threshing the corn, combine harvester,
Threshing the corn, combine harvester,
Threshing the corn, combine harvester,
Chug, chug, chug, chug, chugging away.

5   Big red combine harvester,
Big red combine harvester,
Big red combine harvester,
Chug, chug, chug, chug, chugging away.
Chug, chug, chug, chug, chugging away.

CEREALS, BREAD, VEG AND FRUIT

Words and Music by Anne Blackwell and Niki Davies

Cereals, bread, veg and fruit
Are very good to eat.
Lean meat, poultry, fish and cheese,
A fair amount of each.
A little milk, an egg or two,
Yoghurt and rice are healthy for you,
But too much marg or butter, you'll see
Will take away your energy!

Repeat verse

CONKERS!

Words and Music by Mark and Helen Johnson

CHORUS *Conkers! I'm collecting conkers,*
I'm trying hard to find the biggest and the best.
Conkers! Lots of lovely conkers,
I want a conker that is better than the rest.

1 Under the chestnut tree,
There waits for me
A sight so marv'llous to behold.
Amidst the autumn leaves,
It gleams at me,
A conker, beautiful and bold.

CHORUS

2 Under the chestnut tree,
Where no-one's been,
The spiky shells lie on the ground.
Beneath their armour green,
There hides unseen,
A conker, smooth and shiny brown.

CHORUS

3 Under the chestnut tree,
I stretch to see
A final conker to be mine.
If I can only reach
To pull it free,
I'll add it to my ninety-nine! ONE HUNDRED!

CHORUS *Conkers! Lots of lovely conkers!*
Conkers! Lots of lovely conkers!
(Repeat to fade)

EVERYBODY PRAISE HIM

Words and Music by Mark and Helen Johnson

1   Give thanks to the Lord,
    The giver of life,
    Creator of all,
    The Father of light.
    Give thanks to the Lord
    From morning 'til night,
    Everybody praise Him!

2   Give thanks to the Lord
    In heaven above,
    For all that He's done,
    For all of His love.
    Give thanks to the Lord
    For giving so much,
    Everybody praise Him!

3   *Repeat verse 1*

4 & 5   *Repeat verse 2 with harmony lyrics:*

            Hallelujah! Sing your praises!
            Hallelujah! Sing your praises!

EVERYWHERE AROUND ME

Words and Music by Mark and Helen Johnson

1 Tell me who made all of creation,
   Who designed the wonders of nature?
   Whose idea was pattern and colour,
   Wonderful to see?

   CHORUS *Everywhere around me*
           I can see the hand of God,
           The evidence surrounds me
           In the greatness of His world.
           (Repeat)

2 Tell me who made music and laughter,
   Who designed our bodies to start with?
   Whose idea was thinking and feeling,
   Who gave life to me?

   CHORUS

3 Don't stop looking, don't stop believing,
   God is to be found when you seek Him.
   All creation tells of His glory,
   For eternity.

   CHORUS
           Everywhere around me!

CCLI Song No. 2642310

FIVE A DAY

Words and Music by Niki Davies

CHORUS   *1, 2, 3, 4, 5 a day,*
          1, 2, 3, 4, 5 a day,
          It's got to be the healthy way,
          It's 1, 2, 3, 4, 5,
          Five a day.

1   Apples and bananas too,
     You can take your pick.
     Strawberries and mangos,
     These should do the trick.

     CHORUS

2   Kiwi fruit and peaches too,
     You can take your pick.
     Oranges and juicy pears,
     These should do the trick.

     CHORUS

3   Cabbages and carrots too,
     You can take your pick.
     Aubergines and French beans,
     These should do the trick.

     CHORUS

4   Lettuce and tomatoes too,
     You can take your pick.
     Radishes and shiny peas,
     These should do the trick.

     CHORUS

FOOD COLOURS

Words and Music by Mark and Helen Johnson

1   I went to the shops last Monday
     To buy my Mum some food.
     She said would I make it healthy,
     'Cause colourings aren't so good.
     I went past the crisps and cola
     To find the veg and fruit,
     The shelves were so full of colours
     I didn't know what to do!

     CHORUS   *I bought her (him) a bag of oranges,*
               Some greens and lemons too.
               I tried very hard but couldn't find
               Any blacks or blues!

2   I went to the shops last Tuesday
     To buy my Gran some food.
     She said would I make it healthy,
     'Cause colourings aren't so good.
     I went past the crisps and cola
     To find the veg and fruit,
     The shelves were so full of colours
     I didn't know what to do!

     CHORUS

3   I went to the shops last Wednesday
     To buy my Dad some food.
     He said would I make it healthy,
     'Cause colourings aren't so good.
     I went past the crisps and cola
     To find the veg and fruit,
     The shelves were so full of colours
     I didn't know what to do!

     CHORUS

Good Things

Words and Music by Mark and Helen Johnson

1 Baking bread, country air,
  Freshly laundered clothes to wear,
  Tidy lawns, roses fair,
  Smell so good to me.

2 Tender hands, silky sheets,
  Gentle sand beneath my feet,
  Soothing baths, summer breeze,
  Feel so good to me.

  CHORUS *There are so many good things for us to appreciate.*
  Everybody join in the chorus, we can celebrate!
  (Repeat)

3 Cloudless skies, mountain views,
  When somebody smiles at you,
  A page of ticks, plates of food
  Look so good to me.

4 Juicy fruit – good to eat,
  Bars of chocolate, bags of sweets,
  Fizzy drinks in the heat
  Taste so good to me.

  CHORUS

5 Singing birds, warm "Hellos",
  Music on the radio,
  Loud guitars, saxophones
  Sound so good to me.

  LAST CHORUS
  There are so many good things for us to appreciate.
  Everybody join in the chorus, we can celebrate!
  There are so many good things for us to appreciate.
  Thank the Lord for his loving kindness each and every day!

HARVEST HYMN
(GIVE THANKS)

Words and Music by Mark and Helen Johnson

1   Long before the summer started
Fields were ploughed and sown.
Seeds were scattered, crops were planted,
Now they are full grown.

    CHORUS   *Give thanks for the harvest,*
The sun, the seed, the rain.
Give thanks to God the Father
For harvest time again.

2   April showers and sunny weather
Fed the earth again.
Warmth and moisture both together
Helped to grow the grain.

    CHORUS

3   Every field of golden yellow
Standing in the sun,
Tells how God in all His splendour
Cares for everyone.

    CHORUS

4   Come with thankful hearts and voices,
Come with joyful song,
For the good food all around us,
Now the work is done.

    CHORUS x 2

HARVEST SAMBA

Words and Music by Mark and Helen Johnson

1.   Cabbages and greens,
   Broccoli and beans,
   Cauliflower and roasted potatoes,
   Taste so good to me!

2.   Apricots and plums,
   Ripened in the sun,
   Oranges and yellow bananas,
   Good for everyone!

   CHORUS   *It's another Harvest Festival*
   When we bring our fruit and vegetables,
   'Cause we want to share the best of all
   The good things that we've been given.
   It's another opportunity,
   To be grateful for the food we eat,
   With a samba celebration to
   Say 'Thank you' to God the Father.

3.   Golden corn and wheat,
   Oats and sugar beet,
   Fluffy rice and tasty spaghetti,
   Wonderful to eat!

4.   Coffee, cocoa, tea,
   Growing naturally,
   Herbal plants and all kinds of spices,
   Very nice indeed!

   CHORUS

   MIDDLE 8   *Thank you for the harvest,*
   Thank you for your goodness,
   For all of the fruit and vegetables
   And the wonderful things that grow.
   (Repeat)

   Repeat verses 1 then 2 (with Middle 8)

   CHORUS
       God the Father.

HARVEST SONG

Words and Music by Mark and Helen Johnson

1   There is a farmer who stands in his fields
    And he sees all the work to be done.
    He has been watching for many a month,
    He's been waiting for this day to come.

    CHORUS   *There's a song to sing as the harvest comes in,*
             To the One who gives sunshine and rain.
             Let us all join in with a thank-offering
             For the harvest that's gathered again.

2   There was a time when the fields were prepared
    And the good soil was carefully ploughed.
    Then came the day for the farmer to sow
    And the seeds were all scattered around.

    CHORUS

3   There was some time for the farmer to wait
    As the seeds slowly grew out of sight.
    Then came the day when the first shoots appeared
    And the farmer was filled with delight.

    CHORUS

4   Now is the time when the crops are full grown
    And the farmer must gather them in.
    He'll need some help 'cause there's lots to be done
    And it's hard to know where to begin.

    CHORUS x 2

HARVEST TIME HAS COME

Words and Music by Sha Armstrong

CHORUS *The farmer's in his fields from dawn till dusk,*
Working every hour as he knows he must,
Gathering all the crops till the work is done,
For harvest time has come.

CHORUS

1 Picking off the apples, picking off the pears,
Food we love to eat,
Digging up the carrots, digging up the leeks
Till the harvest is complete.

CHORUS

2 Picking off the sweetcorn, picking off the peas,
Food we love to eat,
Digging up the parsnips, digging up the swedes
Till the harvest is complete.

CHORUS

3 Picking off the berries, picking off the plums,
Food we love to eat,
Digging up potatoes, digging up the beets
Till the harvest is complete, complete.

CHORUS *The farmer's in his fields from dawn till dusk,*
Working every hour as he knows he must,
Gathering all the crops till the work is done,
For harvest time has come,
For harvest time has come,
Harvest time has come.

CCLI Song No. 5182705

In My Trolley

Words and Music by Jeff Hammer

1   Eggs and apples in my trolley,
Eggs and apples in my trolley,
Every time I shop
I should thank God for the 'crop' of
Eggs and apples in my trolley.

2   Milk and carrots in my trolley,
Milk and carrots in my trolley,
Every time I shop
I should thank God for the 'crop' of
Milk and carrots,
Eggs and apples in my trolley.

3   Fish and ice cream in my trolley, …
Fish and ice cream in my trolley,
Every time I shop
I should thank God for the 'crop' of
Fish and ice cream,
Milk and carrots,
Eggs and apples in my trolley.

4   Meat and biscuits in my trolley, …

5   Sweets and lettuce in my trolley, …

6   All the food that's in my trolley,
All the food that's in my trolley,
Every time I shop
I should thank God for the 'crop' of
All the food that's in my trolley!

LUNCHTIME QUEUE

Words and Music by Mark and Helen Johnson

1   Down in my tummy I'm feeling so hungry,
    My mind is on nothing but lovely food.
    When you've not eaten for hours at least then
    You can't help but dream in the lunchtime queue.

    CHORUS   *What's on the menu for lunchtime today?*
             Let me imagine what it might say:

2   Egg-burger, cheese-burger, barbecued bean-burger,
    Guaranteed lean, served with French fries too.
    Tagliatelli with cheese that is smelly,
    To fill up my belly all afternoon.

    CHORUS

3   Jacket potato with salad that tastes so
    Delicious with mayo and good for you.
    Savoury pizza with my favourite meatza,
    So tasty to eat when you're in the mood.

    CHORUS

4   Pineapple fritters with banana splitters and
    Raspberry ripple served with a spoon.
    Strawberry shortcakes with cream, like my mum makes,
    And thick chocolate milkshakes would nicely do.

    CHORUS

5   GROUP 1   I'll tell you what's on the menu –
                 It's cottage pie or stew.
                 Cook has been busy all morning,
                 Her food will have to do!
                 (Repeat)

    GROUP 2   Repeat verse 1 with GROUP 1 on repeat.

MR SCARECROW

Words and Music by Niki Davies

1   Don't go pecking in the cornfield,
    Don't go pecking in the cornfield,
    Don't go pecking in the cornfield,
    'Cause Mister Scarecrow's there!

    CHORUS   *Mister Scarecrow, Mister Scarecrow,*
              Mister Scarecrow is waiting for you.
              Mister Scarecrow, Mister Scarecrow,
              Mister Scarecrow is waiting for you.

2   Mister Birdie, are you listening?
    Mister Birdie, are you listening?
    Mister Birdie, are you listening?
    'Cause Mister Scarecrow's there!

    CHORUS

3   Don't go pecking in the cornfield,
    Don't go pecking in the cornfield,
    Don't go pecking in the cornfield,
    'Cause Mister Scarecrow's there!

    CHORUS

PICTURE OF AUTUMN

Words and Music by Mary Green and Julie Stanley

CHORUS *We can sing a picture of autumn,*
We can paint a melody,
We can sing a picture of autumn
And tell you of the things we see.

1 Leaves of brown – falling down,
Berries red – birds will be fed,
Golden wheat – bread to eat,
Straw and hay – stored away.

CHORUS

2 Morning haze – sunny days,
Squirrels store – hedgehogs snore,
Swallows fly – say goodbye!
Harvest moon – winter soon.

PRAISE TO THE ONE

Words and Music by Mark and Helen Johnson

Praise to the One who made our bodies,
Praise to the One who gives us life.
Praise to the One for all creation,
Praise Him, praise Him, morning and night.

(Repeat 3 times)

SING A SONG FOR HARVEST

Words and Music by Nikki Lewis

1   Sing a song for harvest, sing it loud and clear,
    Sing a song for harvest at this time of year.
    Praise the One who made the stars and the sun,
    Praise the One that gave His gifts to everyone.

    CHORUS   *Praise our God* (clap, clap)*, let's give!*
                Praise our God (clap, clap)*, let's live!*

2   Sing a song for harvest, sing it loud and clear,
    Sing a song for harvest at this time of year.
    Praise the One who made the creatures great and small,
    Praise the One that gave His gifts to one and all.

    CHORUS

3   Sing a song for harvest, sing it loud and clear,
    Sing a song for harvest at this time of year.
    Praise the One who made us every plant and tree,
    Praise the One that gave His gifts to you and me.

    CHORUS

4   Sing a song for harvest, sing it loud and clear,
    Sing a song for harvest at this time of year.
    Praise the One who gave us gifts so we can live,
    Praise the One who taught us TO GIVE.

    CHORUS x 2

SUPER SUN

Words and Music by Niki Davies

1   Hello sun, hello sun,
        Do your work today.
        Shine on down from the sky,
        Don't you go away.
        Turn the corn to yellow,
        Make the berries nice and mellow,
        Super sun, super sun.

2   Hello sun, hello sun,
        Do your work today.
        Shine on down from the sky,
        Don't you go away.
        Make the apples redder
        So the fruit tastes even better,
        Super sun, super sun.

3   Hello sun, hello sun,
        Do your work today.
        Shine on down from the sky,
        Don't you go away.
        Make the wheat grow higher
        And the golden hay stay drier,
        Super sun, super sun.
        Super sun!

THANK YOU FOR ALMOST EVERYTHING!

Words and Music by Mary Green and Julie Stanley

1   Thank you for carrots and peas,
    Thank you for honey from bees,
    Thank you for everything
    Except for brussel sprouts!*

2   Thank you for curry and rice,
    Thank you for strawberry ice,
    Thank you for everything
    Except for mouldy cheese!

3   Thank you for raspberry jam,
    Thank you for bacon and ham,
    Thank you for everything
    Except for pickled eggs!

4   Thank you for barbeque sauce,
    Thank you for ketchup of course,
    Thank you for everything
    Except for garlic snails!

5   Thank you for chicken to roast,
    Thank you for baked beans on toast,
    Thank you for everything
    Except for mushy peas!

6   Thank you for liquorice strings,
    Thank you for chocolaty things,
    Thank you for everything
    Except for sour cream!

7   Thank you for sausage and chips,
    Thank you for grapes with no pips,
    Thank you for everything,
    (Spoken) Well, almost everything,
    Almost everything!

* Last line of each verse can be sung by individual or group.

Thank You for the Sunshine

Words and Music by Mark and Helen Johnson

1   I'm gonna thank you for the sunshine,
Thank you for the rain,
Thank you in the bright times and the dark times.
I'm gonna thank you every morning,
Thank you every day,
Thank you in the good times and the hard times.

    CHORUS   *What an amazing world we live in,*
What an amazing life we have,
So many good things we've been given,
So many reasons to be glad.

2   I'm gonna thank you for the mountains,
Thank you for the seas,
Thank you for the big things and the small things.
I'm gonna thank you for creation,
The very air we breathe,
Thank you for the beauty that's in all things.

    CHORUS

3   I'm gonna thank you for my family,
Thank you for my friends,
Thank you for the times we share together.
I'm gonna thank you for beginnings
And when things have to end,
Thank you for the love that lasts forever.

    CHORUS

4   *Repeat verse 1*

    Thank you in the good times and the hard times.

THANK YOU GOD FOR THE HARVEST

Words and Music by Niki Davies

1   Gather up a box of pears,
    Box of pears, box of pears,
    Gather up a box of pears,
    Thank you, God, for the harvest.

2   Gather up a box of plums,
    Box of plums, box of plums,
    Gather up a box of plums,
    Thank you, God, for the harvest.

3   Gather up a box of apples,
    Box of apples, box of apples,
    Gather up a box of apples,
    Thank you, God, for the harvest.

4   Gather up a box of nuts,
    Box of nuts, box of nuts,
    Gather up a box of nuts,
    Thank you, God, for the harvest.

5   Gather up a box of wheat,
    Box of wheat, box of wheat,
    Gather up a box of wheat,
    Thank you, God, for the harvest.

THE HARVEST OF LOVE

Words and Music by Mary Green and Julie Stanley

1   An empty bowl,
     A crying child,
     A mother filled with dread –
     An empty cup,
     A scorching sun,
     A dried up river bed.

2   An empty sack,
     A crying child,
     A father filled with fear –
     A barren field,
     An empty store,
     The crops have failed this year.

CHORUS   *We must be aware and show that we care,*
          So let's work together in this world we share.
          Let's learn how to give, to help others live,
          And reap the harvest of love.

3   A bowl of maize,
     A smiling child,
     A lorry bringing aid –
     A brimming cup,
     A sheltered home,
     A difference has been made.

4   A sack of maize,
     A smiling child,
     A lorry bringing seed –
     A planted field,
     A waiting store,
     Hope for those in need.

CHORUS
          Reap the harvest of love.

THE HEALTHY HABANERA

Words and Music by Mary Green and Julie Stanley

To be sung with humour!

1   You must eat your fruit and veg you know,
        Make you strong and help your body grow,
        Eyes will sparkle and your skin will glow
        When you eat your five a day.

2   Have a carrot or a tangerine,
        Have a mango or an aubergine,
        Chew on veggies that are shades of green
        And you'll get your five a day.

        BRIDGE   *Just be aware*
                       If you long for shiny hair,
                       Eat lots and lots
                       And you won't come out in spots!

3   If you eat your fruit and veg today
        Then you'll keep disease and germs away,
        It'll help your body work okay
        When you eat your five a day.
        OLÉ!

THE SUN CAME SHINING DOWN

Words and Music by Niki Davies

1   The sun came shining down,
The sun came shining down,
The sun came shining down
And the crops grew higher and higher,
Higher and higher.

2   The rain came tumbling down,
The rain came tumbling down,
The rain came tumbling down
And the crops grew higher and higher,
Higher and higher.

3   The soil was rich and good,
The soil was rich and good,
The soil was rich and good
And the crops grew higher and higher,
Higher and higher.

4   The sun came shining down,
The sun came shining down,
The sun came shining down
And the crops grew higher and higher,
Higher and higher.

THE VEGETABLE SONG

Words and Music by Paul Field

1 I like vegetables, they make me big and strong,
I like vegetables, I eat them all day long,
Spinach and carrots, cauliflower and greens,
Parsnips and broccoli, French beans.
I like vegetables, there's only one left out,
I like vegetables but I don't like sprouts!
I don't like sprouts!

2 I like vegetables, they're very good for me,
I like vegetables, God made them all you see,
Mushrooms and sweetcorn, potatoes old and new,
Cabbage leaves and celery, mange tout.
I like vegetables, there's only one left out,
I like vegetables but I don't like sprouts!
I don't like sprouts!

3 I like vegetables, there's such a lot to choose,
Boiled, fried or roasted, in casseroles and stews,
Onions and aubergines, artichokes and peas,
Filled with vitamins, A B C and D.
I like vegetables, there's only one left out,
I like vegetables but I don't like sprouts!
I don't like sprouts! .
I don't – like –
(Have a potato)
No sprouts!

WE THANK YOU

Words and Music by Sha Armstrong

CHORUS   *We thank you God for all you have given us,*
Families, food and friends.
We thank you God for all you have given us,
For all you've made, we thank you God, amen.

1   For good food we can eat,
For close friends we can meet,
For families all around
Who keep us safe and sound.

CHORUS

2   For picnics in the park,
For sleepovers in the dark,
For families everywhere,
We offer up this prayer…

CHORUS

3   For tea times after school,
For friends who share it all,
For families, yours and mine,
Who love us all the time.

CHORUS

WEIRD AND WONDERFUL

Words and Music by Paul Field

1   Where is the pie in a pineapple?
        Who made bananas bent?
        Just how fast can a runner bean run?
        Why does a Cauliflower have no scent?

        CHORUS   *It's a weird and wonderful world,*
                    Full of tastes so bitter and sweet,
                    It's a weird and wonderful world of food
                    With so much choice of good things to eat.

2   Have you tasted hot goat curry?
        Did you try a horse meat stew?
        Have you had a duck's foot braised in brine
        Or kangaroo steak on the barbecue?

        CHORUS

        INSTRUMENTAL

        CHORUS
                    With so much choice of good things to eat.
                    With so much choice of good things to eat.

WHAT YOU SOW

Words and Music by Ann Beresford

1   If you sow an apple seed, will a pear tree grow?
     If you plant an orange pip, will a raspberry show?
     If you sow a spiteful word, will a friendship grow?
     The answer to all three of these is absolutely "NO!"

     CHORUS   *What you sow is what you'll reap,*
               What you give you will receive,
               Do to others as you'd have them do,
               The outcome of all three of these
               Is absolutely true!

2   If you sow a mustard seed, will a gooseberry grow?
     If you plant a daffodil, will a tulip show?
     If you sow an unkind thought, will a friendship grow?
     The answer to all three of these is absolutely "NO!"

     CHORUS

3   Sow a seed of thoughtfulness, see how love takes root,
     Water it with forgiveness, see it bear much fruit,
     Give it time and lots of care, watch your friendship grow,
     What you sow is what you'll reap,
     Sow love and love will grow.

     CHORUS

© 2008 Out of the Ark Ltd, Middlesex TW12 2HD
CCLI Song No. 5182846

COPYRIGHT & LICENSING - What You Need To Know

The world of copyright and licensing can seem very daunting, particularly because there is an obligation on schools to comply with copyright law. We're here to help you through the process and to keep you legal. The guidelines below explain the most common copyright and licensing issues.

Singing Songs in the Classroom

You are free to use all of the material – including songs and scripts – in the classroom for teaching purposes. If photocopying any part of the book for teaching purposes please record this usage on your school's photocopy log to ensure that you are legally protected.

Singing Songs in an Assembly or in Church

Songs may be sung in assembly without charge. In addition, the CD may be played provided that your school has a PRS licence. However, the reproduction of the lyrics and/or musical scores for use in an assembly or a church requires a licence. The following licences from Christian Copyright Licensing Limited (www.ccli.com) permit the photocopying or reproduction of song lyrics or musical scores – for example to create song sheets, overhead transparencies or to display the lyrics or music using any electronic display medium:

For UK schools: A Collective Worship Copyright Licence and a Music Reproduction Licence
For churches: A Church Copyright and Music Reproduction Licence

The following credit should be included with the lyrics:

'Reproduced by kind permission © Out of the Ark Ltd'

Please ensure that you log the songs that are used on your CCLI and MRL copy report. Your CCLI licence also grants you permission to display the song lyrics from our Words on Screen™ CD ROMS on a whiteboard or other screen. Simply log the song titles on your copy report. Organisations that do not hold one of the above licences should contact Out of the Ark Limited directly for permission.

Singing Songs in a Concert

If you are performing any of our songs for the public on school premises (i.e. to anyone other than pupils or staff) then royalty payments become due. Contact Out of the Ark Music directly to obtain a licence. **Please note:** There is no need to obtain a licence from the publisher if your school has an arrangement with the **Performing Rights Society (PRS)** either directly or through the local authority.

If you are performing songs at a public venue (other than on the school premises or in a church) then the performance should be logged on the venue's PRS report.

The photocopying or reproduction of song lyrics or musical scores for use in concerts – for example to create song sheets, overhead transparencies or to display the lyrics or music using any electronic display medium – requires a licence. Please contact Out of the Ark Music directly.

Making an Audio Recording or a Video of the Performance

If you wish to make an audio or video recording of your performance of any of our works please visit **www.outoftheark.com/licensing** for further information.

Copying and File-sharing

Copying Out of the Ark Music's audio CDs is not permitted without obtaining a licence from the publisher. Installation of Out of the Ark Music's audio CD tracks on to a computer is strictly forbidden without a licence – we can provide schools with a 'Learning Platform Installation Licence'. File-sharing of any of our audio tracks or CD ROM files is strictly prohibited. For more information visit **www.outoftheark.com/licensing**.

Helpful information can be found on the following website:
A Guide to Licensing Copyright in Schools: www.outoftheark.com/licensing
And remember, we are always happy to help. For advice simply contact our customer services team:
Tel: +44 (0)20 8481 7200   Email: copyright@outoftheark.com